THE
DON'T
LAUGH
CHALLENGE®

G.O.A.T
EDITION

D1315861

All-Time Greatest Jokes for Kids - For Boys and Girls Ages 7-12

Don't Laugh Challenge
BONUS PLAY

Join our Joke Club and get the Bonus Play PDF!

Simply send us an email to:

bacchuspublish@gmail.com

and you will get the following:

• 10 BONUS hilarious jokes!

• An entry in our Monthly Giveaway of a
$25 Amazon Gift card!

We draw a new winner each month and will contact you via email!

Good luck!

Welcome to
The Don't Laugh Challenge ®

• How do you play?

The Don't Laugh Challenge is made up of 10 rounds with 2 games in each round. It is a 2-3 player game with the players being 'Goat #1', 'Goat #2', and a 'King' or 'Queen'. In each game you have an opportunity to score points by making the other players laugh.

After completing each round, tally up the points to determine the Round Champion! Add all 10 rounds together to see who is the Ultimate Don't Laugh Challenge Master! If you end up in a tie, use our final Tie Breaker Round for a Winner Takes All!

Who can play the game?
•
Get the whole family involved! Grab a family member or a friend and take turns going back and forth. We've also added Bonus Points in game 2, so grab a 3rd person, a.k.a 'King' or 'Queen', and earn an extra point by making them guess your scene!

The Don't Laugh Challenge®
Activity Rules

- ## Game 1 - Jokes (1 point each)

  Goat #1 will hold the book and read each joke to Goat #2. If the joke makes Goat #2 laugh, Goat #1 can record a point for the joke. Each joke is worth 1 point. At the end of the jokes, tally up your total Joke Points scored for Goat #1 and continue to Game 2!

- ## Game 2 - Silly Scenarios (2 points each + bonus point)

  Without telling the other Goat what the scenarios say, read each scenario to yourself and then get creative by acting it out! You can use sound effects, but be sure not to say any words! If you make the other Goat laugh, record your points and continue to the next scenario.

  BONUS POINT: Get your parents or a third player, a.k.a King or Queen, involved and have them guess what in the world you are doing! Get the King or Queen to guess the scene correctly and you score a BONUS POINT!

The Don't Laugh Challenge®
Activity Rules

Once Goat #1 completes both games it is Goat #2's turn. The directions at the bottom of the book will tell you who goes next. Once you have both completed all the games in the round, add your total points from each game to the Round Score Page and record the Round winner!

- ## How do you get started?

Flip a coin. If guessed correctly, then that Goat begins!

Tip: Make any of the activities extra funny by using facial expressions, funny voices or silly movements!

ROUND
1

Jokes

Why did the pullover take a shower?

/1

It was a SWEAT-er.

What do you call a cinnamon roll that loves ballet?

/1

A-BUN-dance!

Who did the ink have a crush on?

The FINE print!

/1

What's the best hotel for crackers?

/1

The Ritz.

JOKES TOTAL: _____ /4

GOAT 1 CONTINUE TO THE NEXT PAGE ➜

Silly Scenarios

(Act it out!)

Pretend you're a lion and you think you are just the **COOLEST** cat! Walk around on all fours with swagger, lick your front paw and use it to stroke your mane. Look around with confidence as you say, "Me-owwww" or "Rawr" with an attitude!

/2

Pretend you're in a kayak by sitting in a chair and using your arms to steer your paddle. As you paddle away, try to avoid all the rocks and obstacles, but this river you are on is pretty **WILD!** End your exhausting ride by dramatically falling out of your boat!

/2

SILLY SCENARIOS TOTAL: _____ /4

NOW, PASS THE BOOK TO GOAT 2 ➜

Jokes

GOAT 2

How does a goose deal with bad traffic?

It honks!

/1

What sport makes you the sickest?

Hurling.

/1

Why were four out of the five Michigan lakes angry?

Because one thought it was Superior!

/1

What do you call a tuxedo on a scuba diver?

A wet suit!

/1

JOKES TOTAL: _____ /4

GOAT 2 CONTINUE TO THE NEXT PAGE ➜

Silly Scenarios

(Act it out!)

You are an earthworm. Tuck your head into the neckline of your shirt, covering your nose and neck. With only your squinty eyes peeking, wiggle your neck as you slowly reveal the rest of your face from within your shirt. Your wormy self is coming out of the dirt to say, "Hello!"

/2

While bowling with friends, it's your final turn! Act out your swing, as you let go of the ball, and wait for it... You have just scored a triple strike!!! Erupt in your best celebration dance to celebrate your victory!

/2

SILLY SCENARIOS TOTAL: _____ /4

TIME TO SCORE YOUR POINTS! ➤

GOAT 1

/8

ROUND TOTAL

GOAT 2

/8

ROUND TOTAL

ROUND
CHAMPION

ROUND 2

Jokes

GOAT 1

Where do people watch sports and never leave?

STAY-dium.

/1

Why is an insomniac so easy-going?

He's always UP for anything!

/1

Why did the hotel hire the woman?

She was INN-experienced!

/1

Who does an octopus call when his piano is off-key?

A piano TUNA.

/1

JOKES TOTAL: _____ /4

Silly Scenarios

(Act it out!)

You've got an itch on your back, and you can't scratch it with your hands, so it's time to get creative! Roll around and try to scratch it any other way you can, until you finally get that itch scratched!

/2

Act like a crazy monkey that is playing baseball. You are the pitcher and are using poop baseballs! Gross. Make sure you don't get hit by one!

/2

SILLY SCENARIOS TOTAL: _____ /4

Jokes

How many birds can play a video game at the same time?

Toucan!   /1

Why does Superman have an 'S' on his cape?

So he can always es-CAPE!   /1

Do you want to have a picnic at the zoo tomorrow?

Sure, ALPACA lunch!   /1

What did the comb say to the tangled hair?

"Can you knot?"   /1

JOKES TOTAL: _____ /4

GOAT 2 CONTINUE TO THE NEXT PAGE ➝

Silly Scenarios

(Act it out!)

You are looking at your big, juicy burger - YUM! Rub your stomach and lick your lips to show it's something tasty to eat. However, it's SO big that when you try to take a bite, it won't fit in your mouth! Keep trying!

/2

You have to use the bathroom **REALLY** badly, but there is a long line of people (show how you count each person in front of you). You do the 'potty dance' and cross your legs... Will you make it?!

/2

SILLY SCENARIOS TOTAL: _____ /4

TIME TO SCORE YOUR POINTS! ➞

GOAT 1

/8

ROUND TOTAL

GOAT 2

/8

ROUND TOTAL

ROUND CHAMPION

ROUND 3

Jokes

How do toads get so wise?

They POND-er.

/1

What do you call a bear cub that over-eats?

Too much to bear!

/1

Why was the 6th planet named Saturn?

It had a nice RING to it!

/1

Did you hear Scooby Doo started solving underwater mysteries?

/1

He became a Scooby diver.

JOKES TOTAL: _____ /4

Silly Scenarios

(Act it out!)

Demonstrate how to get up and surf giant waves! Unlike other surfers, you have extremely loose and wiggly hips. Show us how you keep your balance and what you look like on a **BIG WAVE!**

_____ /2

Do a silly interpretive dance to show an entire day at school! Make sure to show different subjects, lunch, recess and all the other things that happen during a typical day!

_____ /2

SILLY SCENARIOS TOTAL: _____ /4

NOW, PASS THE BOOK TO GOAT 2 ➜

Jokes

Why did the scuba diver quit?

He couldn't handle the PRESSURE.

/1

What job in sports is best for a puppy?

The Re-FURRY! (Referee)

/1

Why would hockey players put their left foot in and their left foot out?

/1

They are doing the Hockey-Pokey!

What do you call an actor who cares?

/1

A CARE-acter!

JOKES TOTAL: _____ /4

GOAT 2 CONTINUE TO THE NEXT PAGE ➞

26

Silly Scenarios

(Act it out!)

You open a door and walk through - it's FREEZING! You open another door and walk through - Now, it's extremely HOT! You try to go back, but the door won't open. So you sit down wiping the sweat from your head and begin panting!

/2

You are the 'New Laugh Inventor'. Using your finger or a magic wand, each time you touch a different part of your body, you have a completely different laugh! How many different laughs can you create?!

/2

SILLY SCENARIOS TOTAL: _____ /4

TIME TO SCORE YOUR POINTS! ➡

GOAT 1

/8
ROUND TOTAL

GOAT 2

/8
ROUND TOTAL

ROUND CHAMPION

ROUND

4

Jokes

Why did the sheet music need glasses?

/1

It needed to C sharp!

What is a cheerleader's favorite kind of tree?

/1

Palm-palms!

Would you like a number sandwich?

/1

No thanks, I already EIGHT.

Why did the carpenter quit his job?

/1

Well, WOOD you believe he got BOARD?!

JOKES TOTAL: /4

GOAT 1 CONTINUE TO THE NEXT PAGE ➞

30

Silly Scenarios

(Act it out!)

Pretend you drank a magic potion that has turned you into a GIANT! Show us what you would do and how it would look to have a giant walking around the city! (Tip: Get down small when you drink it and then become HUGE!)

/2

You're walking down the street, enjoying your day, when something startles you! Do a quick karate chop and kick your leg in the air, making the noises of "HI-YA!". No one can mess with you!

/2

SILLY SCENARIOS TOTAL: _____ /4

Jokes

GOAT 2

Why was the paperboy fired?

Let's just say he had a lot of ISSUES.

/1

What toy requires your parent's signature to use?

The Permission Slip 'n Slide!

/1

Why do chips and salsa like swimming so much?

They love taking a DIP!

/1

What's a baby fish's favorite game?

Dom-MINNOWS.

/1

JOKES TOTAL: _____ /4

GOAT 2 CONTINUE TO THE NEXT PAGE ➝

Silly Scenarios

(Act it out!)

You have just discovered that you are EXTREMELY ticklish! Try testing out different body parts to see where you are most ticklish, and tickle yourself until you are laughing hysterically on the floor!

_____ /2

It's a strong person contest! Start flexing your muscles, but when you look into the audience, you get super nervous. It's not your friends, but a bunch of wild tigers! Keep flexing your muscles, but show how scared you are by using your facial expressions!

_____ /2

SILLY SCENARIOS TOTAL: _____ /4

TIME TO SCORE YOUR POINTS! ➜

 **GOAT 1** _____ **/8**

ROUND TOTAL

 **GOAT 2** _____ **/8**

ROUND TOTAL

_____

ROUND CHAMPION

ROUND 5

Jokes

GOAT 1

Why did the baby Joey get scolded by his mom?

/1

He was being kanga-RUDE!

What time should you never schedule a dentist appointment?

/1

Tooth-Hurty! (2:30)

What famous landmark do letters go visit?

/1

The Capital.

Why did the two keyboards break-up?

/1

They just weren't each other's TYPE.

JOKES TOTAL: _____ /4

JESTER 1 CONTINUE TO THE NEXT PAGE ➡

Silly Scenarios

(Act it out!)

You're a big dog, walking on all fours. You start growling at something and then jump from being startled! Start whimpering while running in the opposite direction, and don't forget to give your best puppy dog eyes!

/2

You see a giant button in the corner and decide to go over and push it. UH-OH... The button makes you go in reverse! Start walking and dancing backward, while struggling to move forward until you accidentally push it again while dancing, and return back to normal.

/2

SILLY SCENARIOS TOTAL: _____ /4

NOW, PASS THE BOOK TO GOAT 2 ➜

Jokes

What did the bottle say when it realized it was made of aluminum?

/1

"I think I CAN!"

Why did the ketchup go to the salon?

/1

To get her toma-TOES done!

What is an eel's favorite dance?

/1

The electric slide.

What kind of comb should you avoid using in your hair?

/1

Honeycomb!

JOKES TOTAL: _____ /4

GOAT 2 CONTINUE TO THE NEXT PAGE ➡

Silly Scenarios

(Act it out!)

You're a robot, just trying to get ready in the morning (brush your teeth, comb your hair, get dressed), but you keep freezing up at the oddest moments. The only way to unfreeze is to let out a loud and very sudden, "BEEP!" Don't let that stop you from finishing getting ready!

/2

Show us all the amazing moves you have as the 'World's Greatest Trick Ping-Pong Player'. Use your whole body and get creative, so you don't miss the shot!

/2

SILLY SCENARIOS TOTAL: _____ /4

TIME TO SCORE YOUR POINTS! ➡

GOAT 1

/8

ROUND TOTAL

GOAT 2

/8

ROUND TOTAL

ROUND CHAMPION

ROUND

6

Jokes

GOAT 1

Why did the mollusk join the baseball team?

He was born to be a SLUGGER.

/1

What did the hose say to the flowers that needed water?

"Sorry, I MIST you!"

/1

Was the ballet any good?

Yes, it was En Pointe!

/1

Why was the pediatrician so sarcastic?

She was always KID-ding around!

/1

JOKES TOTAL: _____ /4

Silly Scenarios

(Act it out!)

GOAT 1

Pretend you're a zombie cheerleader encouraging the zombie basketball players during a game! While you do your cheer, make sure to groan, moan, and move like the creepy zombie you are!

___/2

You've just entered a pizza eating contest. Rip, fold, and take big bites of your entire pizza, as fast as you can! Chug your water and stand up tall to claim **VICTORY!**

___/2

SILLY SCENARIOS TOTAL: ___/4

NOW, PASS THE BOOK TO GOAT 2 ➡

Jokes

GOAT 2

What do you call an arrogant dog?

A COCKY-spaniel.

/1

Why did the soap profess its innocence?

It knew it was clean!

/1

What did the frog wizard wear to disappear?

His invisibility CROAK.

/1

What did the parachute say to the skydiver?

/1

"I'm falling for YOU!"

JOKES TOTAL: _____ /4

Silly Scenarios

(Act it out!)

You are an opera singer, but you can only sing the names of your friends over and over. Break their hearts and make them laugh until they cry by bellowing their names over and over again! Don't forget to use different octaves!

/2

Act like a spastic, flapping bird crossing the street and dodging cars. Make sure to look both ways!

/2

SILLY SCENARIOS TOTAL: _____ /4

TIME TO SCORE YOUR POINTS! ➝

 GOAT 1 _____ **/8**
ROUND TOTAL

 GOAT 2 _____ **/8**
ROUND TOTAL

_____
ROUND
CHAMPION

ROUND

7

Jokes

GOAT 1

What tells time and stops it?

A stopwatch!

/1

Why couldn't the statue cry?

It had a heart of stone!

/1

What is the strongest bet possible?

The ALPHA-bet!

/1

What do you call a receipt for a roof?

PROOF!

JOKES TOTAL: _____ /4

GOAT 1 CONTINUE TO THE NEXT PAGE →

Silly Scenarios

(Act it out!)

Pretend to be an elderly person that is hunching over and walking with a cane. Slowly, bend down to grab a piece of candy off the ground and eat it. Turns out it was MAGIC CANDY! You suddenly stand up straight, throw the cane away, and leap in the air kicking your feet together! Woo-hoo!

/2

You are a hyper squirrel trying to open a present. Do everything you can to get it open - jump on it, grab it, bite it, ANYTHING! Until you finally get it open!

/2

SILLY SCENARIOS TOTAL: _____ /4

Jokes

What do you call an academy where you learn to take selfies?

/1

Insta-GRAM-mar school.

Can you learn good posture from a book?

/1

Yes, their spines are perfectly straight.

Where do Olympians keep their money?

/1

The pole vault!

What coastal structure weighs the least?

/1

A LIGHT-house.

JOKES TOTAL: _____ /4

GOAT 2 CONTINUE TO THE NEXT PAGE →

Silly Scenarios

(Act it out!)

Demonstrate painting a masterpiece in a very exaggerated manner. Make the wackiest facial expressions and silly sounds for each stroke as you paint! Then, once you're done, stand back and admire your masterpiece!

/2

It's the homecoming halftime show and you are killing it by playing the drums in the marching band! Don't forget to march, jump, and give it your ALL to really get the crowd going!

/2

SILLY SCENARIOS TOTAL: _____ /4

TIME TO SCORE YOUR POINTS! ➔

 **GOAT 1** _____ **/8**
ROUND TOTAL

 **GOAT 2** _____ **/8**
ROUND TOTAL

_____

ROUND
CHAMPION

ROUND

8

Jokes

What's a pig's favorite candy?

A Jolly Rancher!

/1

How do you make mom say, "Wow!"?

Turn this book upside down.

/1

How is a football player different than a fisherman?

One gets tackled, the other has tackle.

/1

What did the bodybuilder say when he was late for the gym?

"Don't WEIGHT for me!"

/1

JOKES TOTAL: _____ /4

Silly Scenarios

(Act it out!)

You are feeling very hot (fanning yourself, panting, etc.), so you get a popsicle from the freezer. You open the package and take a lick, but your tongue gets stuck to the popsicle and you can't yank it off! Keep trying!

/2

Act like a skilled 'Ninja Chef'. You may use your hands and your sword to do all of the chopping! When you're done, put your knife down and strike your final and best Ninja pose!

/2

SILLY SCENARIOS TOTAL: _____ /4

NOW, PASS THE BOOK TO GOAT 2 ➜

Jokes

What do you call an eight-legged race?

A spi-DERBY!

/1

What toys do green lights like to play with?

LE-GO's!

/1

What is lightning's favorite part of a camera?

The flash, of course.

/1

What has a head and a tail, but no body?

A coin!

/1

JOKES TOTAL: _____ /4

GOAT 2 CONTINUE TO THE NEXT PAGE ➔

Silly Scenarios

(Act it out!)

After being sent back in time, you discover that you're a knight competing in a jousting competition! Strap on your armor, mount your trusty horse and gallop forward as you try to attack your opponent with your lance!

/2

You are a toy that's not supposed to be moving in front of humans. QUICK! Freeze in an action pose and gently fall over, so no one suspects a thing...

/2

SILLY SCENARIOS TOTAL: _____ /4

TIME TO SCORE YOUR POINTS! ➔

GOAT 1

/8

_____
ROUND TOTAL

GOAT 2

/8

_____
ROUND TOTAL

_____

ROUND
CHAMPION

ROUND

9

Jokes

Why does the rabbit farmer always wear a big hat when it's sunny outside?

He only has a little HARE! ____ /1

How do you count buildings in Fortnite?

One by one! ____ /1

My grandma always orders her steak "very rare"... I don't know how they keep finding them!

____ /1

Why is it easy to play a prank on a fish?

____ /1

They always take the bait!

JOKES TOTAL: ____ /4

Silly Scenarios

(Act it out!)

Make an entire banana split, from the bottom banana to the final cherry on top! Make sure you make it a fun show, but you are only allowed to use one hand!

/2

As you try on the following shoes: high heels, fireman boots, flip flops, surgeon booties, and slippers, imitate the actions and characteristics of the person who would wear them. You can use actions, sounds, and noises! (Remember **NO** words!)

/2

SILLY SCENARIOS TOTAL: _____ /4

Jokes

What do you call a floor mat with pixie dust on it?

A magic carpet.

/1

What is a bee's favorite kind of hairstyle?

The BUZZ-cut!

/1

Which cheese is never happy?

BLEU cheese!

/1

What do you call a sea creature with a bad attitude?

Crabby!

/1

JOKES TOTAL: _____ /4

Silly Scenarios

(Act it out!)

Congratulations! You are accepting your bouquet and crown for winning the Miss/Mr America pageant! Make sure to do a "**WOW**" face and bring on the waterworks!

/2

You are in a dance battle and for the winning move, you pull out the classic 'Running Man' dance. Show them how it's done!

/2

SILLY SCENARIOS TOTAL: _____ /4

TIME TO SCORE YOUR POINTS! ➝

GOAT 1

/8

_____
ROUND TOTAL

GOAT 2

/8

_____
ROUND TOTAL

_____

ROUND CHAMPION

ROUND
10

Jokes

What do beavers get to drink at restaurants?

A BEAVER-age.

/1

Why do painters have bright smiles?

Well, they do BRUSH a lot!

/1

How do football players carry their stuff?

In sacks.

/1

What's the archer's favorite store?

/1

Target.

JOKES TOTAL: _____ /4

Silly Scenarios

(Act it out!)

You're at the dentist's office, laid back with your mouth open (make the sound of a drill). Your eyes go big and you grab your cheeks and try to close your mouth, but it isn't working!
Look around frantically, and then pretend to pass out! _____ /2

You are a confused duck, walking backward, and trying to find where you left your home. Keep looking and don't forget to add a questionable "Quack!?" every now and then.

_____ /2

SILLY SCENARIOS TOTAL: _____ /4

NOW, PASS THE BOOK TO GOAT 2 ➜

Jokes

What king has a lot of pride?

Lion King!

/1

What has dozens of keys, but none of them unlock anything?

A computer!

/1

What is a Tesla's favorite element?

CAR-bon.

/1

What is a sculptor's favorite toy?

Marbles!

/1

JOKES TOTAL: _____ /4

GOAT 2 CONTINUE TO THE NEXT PAGE ➞

Silly Scenarios

(Act it out!)

You are a famous race car driver, competing for the championship! Your biggest rival is trying their best to run you off the racetrack. Run around in circles while driving your race car, and try to crash your rival before he crashes you! Show if you won or lost!

/2

You are a Tyrannosaurus Rex trying to cook dinner. Try to stir your pots, put dishes in the oven, and taste test them with your tiny little arms!

/2

SILLY SCENARIOS TOTAL: _____ /4

TIME TO SCORE YOUR POINTS! ➞

 **GOAT 1** _____ **/8**
ROUND TOTAL

 **GOAT 2** _____ **/8**
ROUND TOTAL

_____

ROUND
CHAMPION

**ADD UP ALL YOUR POINTS FROM EACH ROUND.
THE PLAYER WITH THE MOST POINTS IS CROWNED
THE ULTIMATE DON'T LAUGH CHALLENGE MASTER!**

**IN THE EVENT OF A TIE, CONTINUE TO
ROUND 11 FOR THE TIE-BREAKER ROUND!**

 **GOAT 1**   _____
GRAND TOTAL

 **GOAT 2**   _____
GRAND TOTAL

_____

**THE ULTIMATE
DON'T LAUGH CHALLENGE MASTER**

ROUND

11

Tie-Breaker
(Winner Takes All!)

Jokes

What group of superheroes are great at finding things?

Sc-AVENGERS!

/1

Why was the bird sick?

It came down with the FLEW!

/1

What does a dog wear when he's feeling fancy?

A pantsuit and bow-wow tie.

/1

Why did the kid dress as a ghost for the pep rally?

He wanted to show school SPIRIT!

/1

JOKES TOTAL: _____ /4

Silly Scenarios

(Act it out!)

GOAT 1

You are a **Billy** goat climbing a mountain to escape the cheetah that is after you! Bounce and leap from spot to spot using all fours, as you make your getaway! (TIP: Make goat noises to really make it believable!)

___/2

Woah, you're riding the roller coaster of a lifetime! Hold out your fists before you run at full speed, dipping high, low, and even doing loop-the-loops. Don't get TOO dizzy!

___/2

SILLY SCENARIOS TOTAL: _____ /4

NOW, PASS THE BOOK TO GOAT 2 ➡

Jokes

What do you call your sibling that you cook soup with?

Your BROTH-er.

/1

Why do you never tell butter any secrets?

It spreads so fast!

/1

What detergent do sailors use?

Tide.

/1

What do you call it when a mountain opens one eye?

/1

Peaking!

JOKES TOTAL: _____ /4

Silly Scenarios

(Act it out!)

You are brushing your teeth, then you gargle and floss. As you are flossing, the floss gets stuck in your teeth! You keep trying to pull it out, but as you're pulling it just keeps going, and going, and going! The floss is **NEVER ENDING!**

/2

You are the star of the ballet! Be a ballerina leaping and twirling across the stage! Ending with the big finale, give them your best final pose and bow!

/2

SILLY SCENARIOS TOTAL: _____ /4

TIME TO SCORE YOUR POINTS! ➜

ADD UP ALL YOUR POINTS FROM THE
PREVIOUS ROUND. THE JESTER WITH
THE MOST POINTS IS CROWNED
THE ULTIMATE DON'T LAUGH CHALLENGE MASTER!

GOAT 1 _____ **/8**
GRAND TOTAL

GOAT 2 _____ **/8**
GRAND TOTAL

_____

**THE ULTIMATE
DON'T LAUGH CHALLENGE MASTER**

Check out our

Visit us at

www.DontLaughChallenge.com

to check out our newest books!

other joke books!

If you have enjoyed our book, we would love for you to review us on Amazon!

Made in the USA
Columbia, SC
25 November 2020